FINN FLIPS

by Cari Meister
Illustrations by Gary Swift

Check out the shark facts in this book and the picture glossary at the back!

SCHOLASTIC INC.

For Aaron, Ben, and Charlie...Forever Flipping! — C.M.
Dedicated to Sara, Jessica, and Jacob — G.S.

ISBN 978-0-545-61738-3

Text copyright © 2014 by Cari Meister.
Illustrations copyright © 2014 by Gary Swift.

All rights reserved. Published by Scholastic Inc.
SCHOLASTIC and associated logos are trademarks and/or registered
trademarks of Scholastic Inc.

12 11 10 9 8 7 6 5 4 3   15 16 17 18 19/0

Printed in the U.S.A.   40
First printing, January 2014

Book design by Maria Mercado

This is Finn.

Finn is great at flips.

Look at Finn!

Finn flips.

Finn flips and flips.

Mako sharks can jump 20 feet into the air.

Oh no!
Watch out!

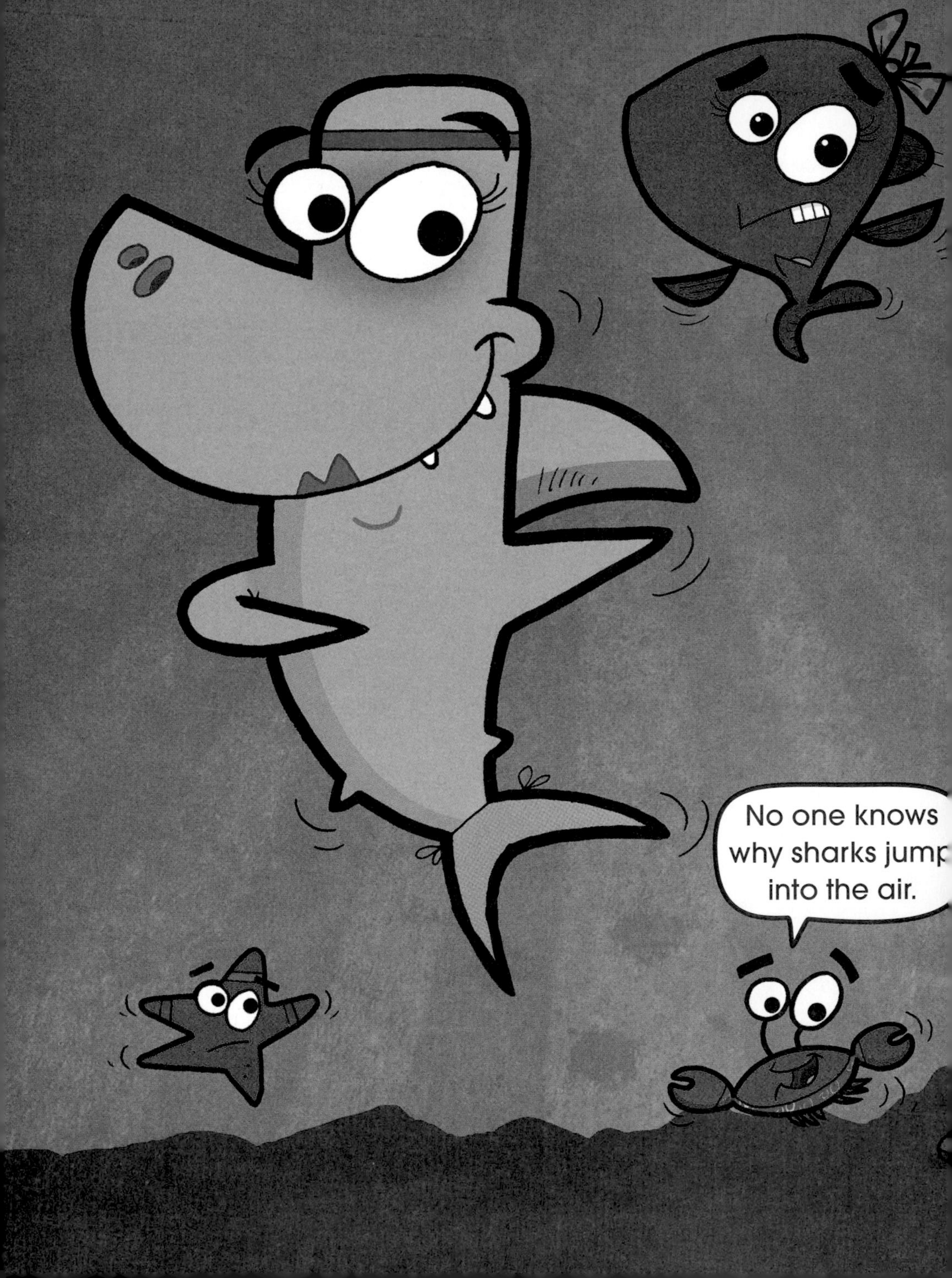

Finn loves to flip.

But Finn always crashes.

Finn crashes
into the lap pool.

Sharks do not sleep.

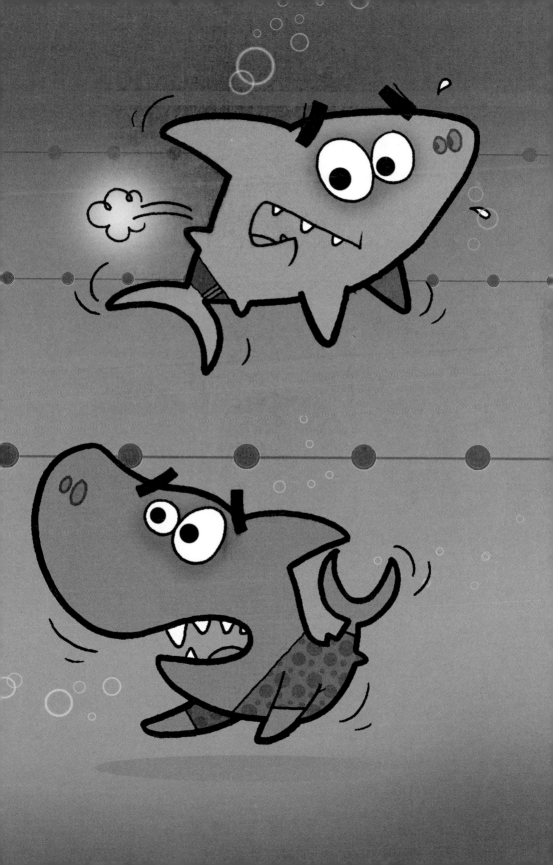

Finn crashes into the snack shop.

Mako sharks eat fish, **eels**, and turtles.

Finn crashes
into the spa.

The other sharks are mad.
"No more flips!" they say.

"Go away!" they say.

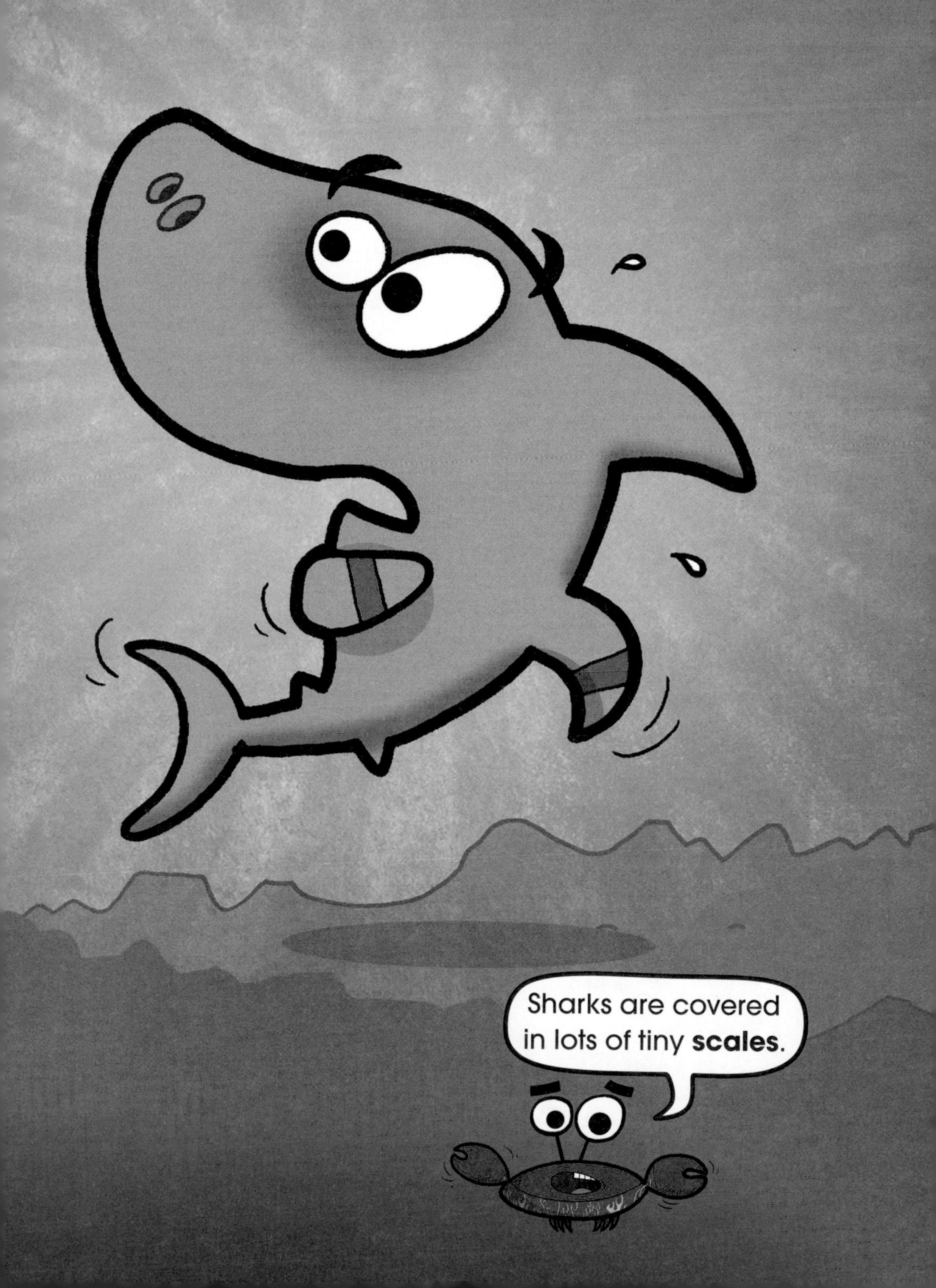

Finn is sad.

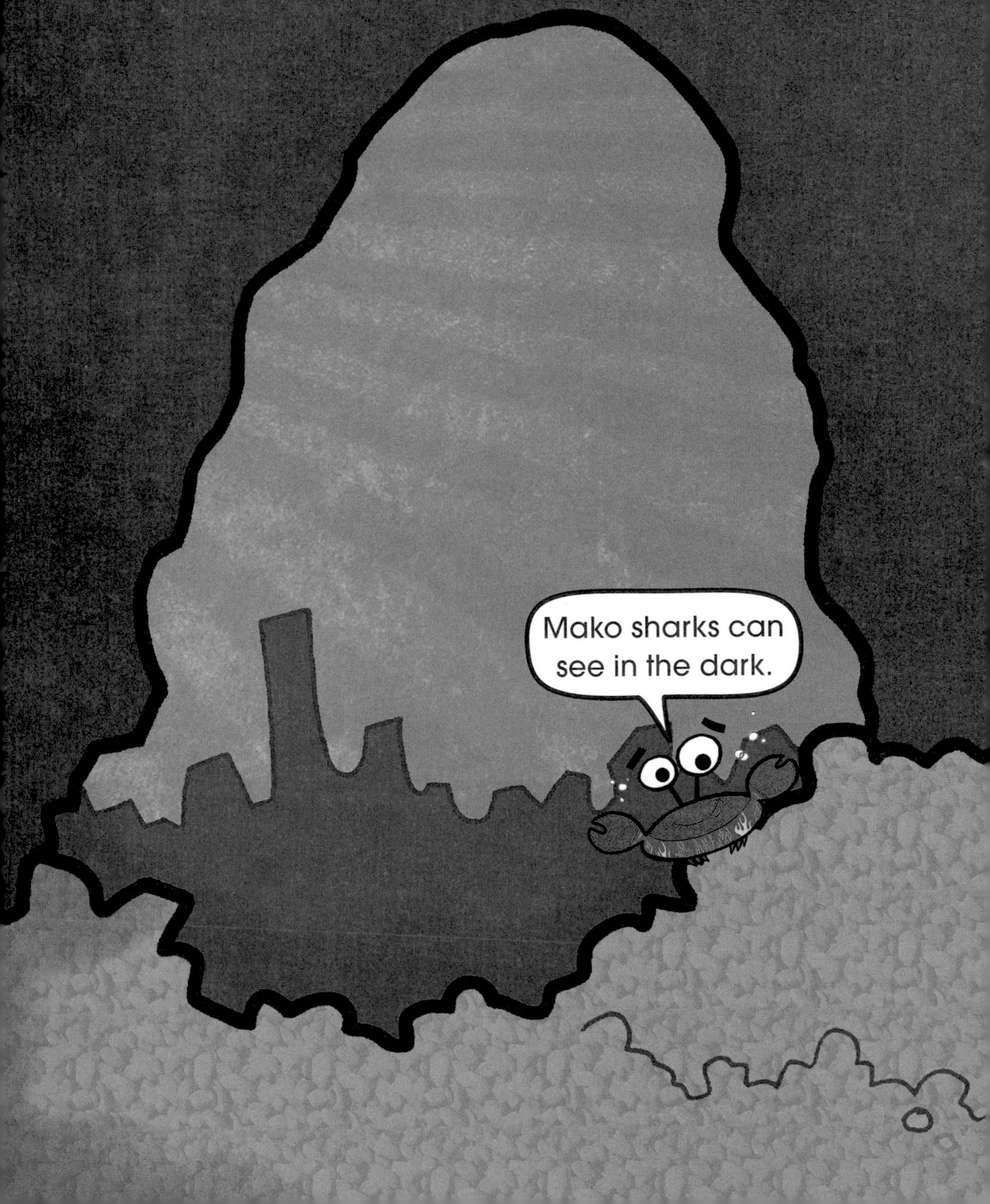

Zelda finds Finn.
She wants to help.

Mako sharks have long, thin teeth.

"You are good at flips,"
says Zelda.
"You just need more room."

Zelda gets ribbon.
She gets shells.

Zelda makes a sign.

Sharks come.
Sharks flip.
Sharks flip and flip.

There are more than 375 kinds of sharks.

But not as high as Finn!

SOME WORDS YOU MAY NOT KNOW

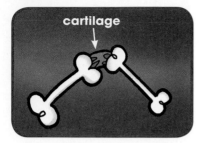

cartilage (KAR-tuh-lij) – strong bendy stuff that connects bones

eel – a long fish that looks like a snake

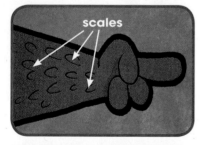

scales – hard bits of skin that cover the bodies of fish, snakes, and lizards

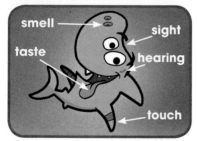

sense – one of the five ways people and animals learn about their surroundings. The five senses are smell, touch, taste, hearing, and sight.

snout – the long front part of an animal's head that includes the mouth and nose